THE BOOK OF 2 Samuel

ONE CHAPTER A DAY

GoodMorningGirls.org

The Book of 2 Samuel

Welcome to Good Morning Girls! We are so glad you are joining us.

God created us to walk with Him, to know Him, and to be loved by Him. He is our living well, and when we drink from the water He continually provides, His living water will change the entire course of our lives.

> *Jesus said: "Whoever drinks of the water that I will give him will never be thirsty again. The water that I will give him will become in him a spring of water welling up to eternal life." ~ John 4:14 (ESV)*

So let's begin.

The method we use here at GMG is called the **SOAK** method.

- ☐ **S**—The S stands for ***Scripture***—Read the chapter for the day. Then choose 1-2 verses and write them out word for word. (There is no right or wrong choice—just let the Holy Spirit guide you.)

- ☐ **O**—The O stands for ***Observation***—Look at the verse or verses you wrote out. Write 1 or 2 observations. What stands out to you? What do you learn about the character of God from these verses? Is there a promise, command or teaching?

- ☐ **A**—The A stands for ***Application***—Personalize the verses. What is God saying to you? How can you apply them to your life? Are there any changes you need to make or an action to take?

- ☐ **K**—The K stands for ***Kneeling in Prayer***—Pause, kneel and pray. Confess any sin God has revealed to you today. Praise God for His word. Pray the passage over your own life or someone you love. Ask God to help you live out your applications.

SOAK God's word into your heart and squeeze every bit of nourishment you can out of each day's scripture reading. Soon you will find your life transformed by the renewing of your mind!

Walk with the King!

Courtney

WomenLivingWell.org, GoodMorningGirls.org

Join the GMG Community

*Share your daily SOAK on **Facebook.com/GoodMorningGirlsWLW***

Instagram: WomenLivingWell #GoodMorningGirls

GMG Bible Coloring Chart

COLORS	KEYWORDS
PURPLE	God, Jesus, Holy Spirit, Saviour, Messiah
PINK	women of the Bible, family, marriage, parenting, friendship, relationships
RED	love, kindness, mercy, compassion, peace, grace
GREEN	faith, obedience, growth, fruit, salvation, fellowship, repentance
YELLOW	worship, prayer, praise, doctrine, angels, miracles, power of God, blessings
BLUE	wisdom, teaching, instruction, commands
ORANGE	prophecy, history, times, places, kings, genealogies, people, numbers, covenants, vows, visions, oaths, future
BROWN/GRAY	Satan, sin, death, hell, evil, idols, false teachers, hypocrisy, temptation

Introduction to the Book of 2 Samuel

The book of 2 Samuel features the life of King David with all his faults and failures, as both a father and a king. It displays the heart of David –both the good and the bad, while also displaying God's grace and judgment. David had a heart of repentance but there were consequences for his sin. But even in the midst of the trials and difficulties David faced, God remained faithful to him.

David was a good king, who loved the Lord and loved his people. He was patient, humble, and courageous. God blessed David with military victories and successes. God made a covenant with David that he would establish his house, kingdom and throne forever. It is through the line of David that the Messiah would come.

Author: Originally, 1 and 2 Samuel were a single book. It is believed that Samuel was the author along with Nathan and Gad.

Date: around 960 BC.

Key Verse: *"The Lord is my rock and my fortress and my deliverer, my God, my rock, in whom I take refuge."* 2 Samuel 22:2

Outline:

1. **David becomes king of Judah and Israel (1-5)**

2. **God establishes David's kingdom (6-10)**

3. **David sins and faces the consequences (11-12)**

4. **David's son rebels against him (13-18)**

5. **God restores David's reign (19-22)**

6. **David's last words and sacrifice (23-24)**

We are all capable of falling into many sins. Even when we have a heart hot for Jesus, we are susceptible to temptation. David's example of giving into temptation when he saw Bathsheba, is a warning to all of us. We must be on guard and never think we are above falling. Proverbs 16:18 tells us: Pride comes before a great fall.

I can't wait to take this journey through 2 Samuel with you!

Let's get started.

Keep walking with the King!

And David lamented.

2 Samuel 1:17

Reflection Question:

David felt deep sorrow over the death of Saul and Jonathan and he lamented. One-third of the Psalms are lamentations. Have you learned to lament?

Much of a Christian's prayer time consists of praise, confession, petitions and thanksgiving. But God wants us to take our grief, sorrows and pain to him also. He knows of your suffering and losses—He is there for you when you cry. Is there something that is hurting you today? Take it to the Lord in prayer and write your lamentation below.

2 Samuel 1

S—The S stands for *Scripture*

O—The O stands for *Observation*

A—The A stands for *Application*

K—The K stands for *Kneeling in Prayer*

David inquired of the Lord.

2 Samuel 2:1

Reflection Question:

David constantly inquired of the Lord for direction. He wanted to be right in the center of God's will.

God has a plan for your life too. His will is that you obey Him. He will never lead you to disobedience of His Word. But is there a decision for your life, that you need to inquire of the Lord about? Ask Him now.

Remember God is for you. If you are truly seeking His will, you can trust Him as He guides you.

S—The S stands for *Scripture*

O—The O stands for *Observation*

A—The A stands for *Application*

K—The K stands for *Kneeling in Prayer*

There was a long war between

the house of Saul and the house of David.

And David grew stronger and stronger,

while the house of Saul

became weaker and weaker.

2 Samuel 3:1

Reflection Question:

In Israel's history, Israel always prevailed when God was with them and they failed when God was not with them. Saul's house relied on human methods and strategies but David depended on God. David prevailed.

Like David, we can overcome the giants in our life when we depend on the Lord. The more we depend on God, the stronger we become. In what area of your life do you need to stop strategizing and start depending on God?

S—The S stands for *Scripture*

O—The O stands for *Observation*

A—The A stands for *Application*

K—The K stands for *Kneeling in Prayer*

{The Lord} has redeemed my life

out of every adversity.

2 Samuel 4:9

Reflection Question:

Two brothers sought to be rewarded by David, for murdering the son of Saul. Rather than being rewarded, they were punished by being put to death. David brought swift justice showing his loyalty to both God and Saul's house.

The two brothers in this story thought they were doing good. They thought David would be pleased and perhaps that they would be closer to David as a result. But they were wrong. Have you ever used gossip—which harms another—in hopes of building a deeper relationship with a friend? In what ways is it harmful and how can you be on guard against this temptation in your life?

2 Samuel 4

S—The S stands for ***Scripture***

O—The O stands for ***Observation***

A—The A stands for ***Application***

K—The K stands for ***Kneeling in Prayer***

And David became greater and greater,

for the Lord, the God of hosts,

was with him.

2 Samuel 5:10

Reflection Question:

David did not start out great. He went through many trials and difficulties, as God prepared him for his role as King. David became great because the Lord, the God of hosts, was with him.

Very few are overnight successes. There is a price for greatness and it often includes pain and difficulty, as God prepares us for the role he has for us. What difficulty have you been through, that you know God allowed to happen to you, to prepare you or strengthen you, for something greater?

2 Samuel 5

S—The S stands for *Scripture*

O—The O stands for *Observation*

A—The A stands for *Application*

K—The K stands for *Kneeling in Prayer*

King David leaped and danced

before the Lord.

2 Samuel 6:16

Reflection Question:

David danced before the Lord. This showed David's genuine emotion and heartfelt worship of God. He was not ashamed to publicly exalt God.

When you worship, do you show emotion or do you repress it in fear of what others might think or say about you? We don't think much of a football player dancing when he makes a touchdown or raising our hands in celebration when our child makes a goal. Do you struggle to express yourself in genuine worship or do you feel free to lift your voice and hands in praise?

2 Samuel 6

S—The S stands for **Scripture**

O—The O stands for **Observation**

A—The A stands for **Application**

K—The K stands for **Kneeling in Prayer**

You are great, O Lord God.

For there is none like you,

and there is no God besides you.

2 Samuel 7:22

Reflection Question:

David did not see himself as great but rather he saw God as great. More than 10 times in this passage, David calls himself a servant. David had a heart of humility and he longed to do more for God.

Sometimes, due to our own selfishness, we can be tempted to do as little as possible for God. David had a heart that was willing to go above and beyond because he saw God's greatness. Sit and ponder for a moment on the greatness of God. List 5 ways that God is great and one way that you can show God a humble servant's heart.

2 Samuel 7

S—The S stands for *Scripture*

O—The O stands for *Observation*

A—The A stands for *Application*

K—The K stands for *Kneeling in Prayer*

And the Lord gave victory to David

wherever he went.

2 Samuel 8:14

Reflection Question:

David is generally known as the greatest King of Israel because of the victories and prosperity that Israel experienced, during David's reign. God wanted to reign in the life of Saul but Saul rejected God. Because David had a heart after God, God was able to use him and bless his people through him.

Can you recall a time in your life when you were like Saul and you resisted the Lord? Can you now see the blessings you missed out on? How can you fully surrender to God now, so that he is able to more fully use you to be a blessing to others around you?

S—The S stands for *Scripture*

O—The O stands for *Observation*

A—The A stands for *Application*

K—The K stands for *Kneeling in Prayer*

So Mephibosheth ate at David's table,

like one of the king's sons.

2 Samuel 9:11

Reflection Question:

The picture of David inviting Mephibosheth to dine at his table, is a beautiful picture of grace. Mephibosheth was in hiding, fearful that he'd be put to death because he was a descendant of Saul. Instead, he was blessed.

David gives us a pattern of serving others in this passage. Who can you seek out to bless? Is there someone undeserving, who is weak, poor, and hidden, who you can show the kindness of God to? Follow David's example. Be a blessing to someone who is undeserving today.

S—The S stands for *Scripture*

O—The O stands for *Observation*

A—The A stands for *Application*

K—The K stands for *Kneeling in Prayer*

Be of good courage.

2 Samuel 10:12

Reflection Question:

Joab called on his people to have strength and courage as they went into battle. He wisely trusted in God for the outcome, while simultaneously working hard for the victory.

Courage is a choice. Is there a battle you are fighting, that requires courage and strength? This is your call to courage. May the Lord fight your battle, as you step up courageously and face whatever the Lord is calling you to.

S—The S stands for *Scripture*

O—The O stands for *Observation*

A—The A stands for *Application*

K—The K stands for *Kneeling in Prayer*

The thing that David had done

displeased the Lord.

2 Samuel 11:27

Reflection Question:

When David was tempted, instead of fleeing temptation—he brought temptation closer. He acted on impulse and pursued the temptation and chose to fall into sin.

What temptation are you struggling with today? Naming your temptation is the first step to overcoming it. We all are tempted in many ways. You do not need to be ashamed of feeling tempted. But we do need to be on guard, because all temptations begin in the heart and mind. Repent of any sin in your life that you have pursued and get help if you are not able to overcome a temptation in your life. God will forgive you and he wants to strengthen you today.

S—The S stands for *Scripture*

O—The O stands for *Observation*

A—The A stands for *Application*

K—The K stands for *Kneeling in Prayer*

David said

"I have sinned against the Lord."

2 Samuel 12:13

Reflection Question:

David took responsibility for his sin. He didn't blame-shift, rationalize, minimize or justify his actions. Though David's sin was against Uriah and Bathsheba, he recognized that ultimately it was against God. After his confession, David received both immediate forgiveness and immediate consequences for his sin.

Do you realize that all sin is ultimately, against God? Is there a sin you need to confess today? Whether the sin seems big or small, if God is bringing it to mind, confess it. Confession does not need to be a long or drawn out. It is a purifying process and you will find immediate forgiveness from your loving Savior.

2 Samuel 12

S—The S stands for *Scripture*

O—The O stands for *Observation*

A—The A stands for *Application*

K—The K stands for *Kneeling in Prayer*

When King David heard
of all these things,
he was very angry.

2 Samuel 13:21

Reflection Question:

David was angry when he heard of his son's dreadful behavior but he did nothing! He failed as a father to discipline his son and protect his daughter. David's failure as a parent came because of his own sin and impurities.

If you are a parent, God is calling you to train your children to walk in obedience to Him. Whether you have sinned in the past and your child is repeating your sin or not—you must address the sin in your children's lives. If you don't, who will? Is there someone in your life who is living in sin who you need to gently correct? Write a prayer asking God to open a door for you to boldly speak truth into the life of your loved one.

2 Samuel 13

S—The S stands for *Scripture*

O—The O stands for *Observation*

A—The A stands for *Application*

K—The K stands for *Kneeling in Prayer*

Now in all Israel

there was no one so much to be praised

for his handsome appearance as Absalom.

2 Samuel 14:25

Reflection Question:

Israel loved King Saul because he was attractive and once again, Israel loved Absalom because of his handsome appearance. In chapter 15, we are told that Absalom stole the hearts of the men of Israel. Man looks at the outside appearance, but God looks at the heart.

Is there someone in your life today, who you are drawn to simply because of his or her outward appearance? What is this person's heart like? Remember to be on guard against appearances. Man looks at the outside but God looks at the heart.

2 Samuel 14

S—The S stands for *Scripture*

O—The O stands for *Observation*

A—The A stands for *Application*

K—The K stands for *Kneeling in Prayer*

May the Lord show steadfast love

and faithfulness to you.

2 Samuel 15:20

Reflection Question:

David had shown great grace to Absalom, yet Absalom turned on David and betrayed him. David never blamed God for his difficulties. David continued to trust in God's goodness despite, once again, being on the run in fear of his life.

Have you grown weary in doing good? Perhaps you have trusted in God's goodness through a difficult trial, only to find yourself once again in another heavy trial. God is with you and he will carry you through. Take your trial to the Lord in prayer today, as a commitment to continue to trust in God.

S—The S stands for **Scripture**

O—The O stands for **Observation**

A—The A stands for **Application**

K—The K stands for **Kneeling in Prayer**

It may be that the Lord
will look on the wrong done to me,
and that the Lord
will repay me with good.
2 Samuel 16:12

Reflection Question:

Rather than taking the situation into his own hands, David was willing to be at God's mercy. He trusted that if he did was right in the moment, God would take care of his future.

Has someone treated you unfairly or unkindly? Perhaps you are tempted to retaliate or treat them poorly in return. What do you think God wants you to do? Could you give this person mercy and trust that God will take care of you rather than taking the matter into your own hands?

2 Samuel 16

S—The S stands for **Scripture**

O—The O stands for **Observation**

A—The A stands for **Application**

K—The K stands for **Kneeling in Prayer**

The people are hungry and weary

and thirsty in the wilderness.

2 Samuel 17:29

Reflection Question:

God provided friends for David in the wilderness. They were sent by God to comfort him during his affliction and to stand by him, so he was not alone.

Do you have a friend who has stood by you through a trial? That friend was a gift from God. Be sure to thank her for being there for you.

Who do you know who is going through a trial right now that you can stand by and comfort? Take the time to reach out to that friend today through a simple text, email, phone call, hug, cup of coffee or card in the mail.

S—The S stands for *Scripture*

O—The O stands for *Observation*

A—The A stands for *Application*

K—The K stands for *Kneeling in Prayer*

Blessed be the Lord your God.

2 Samuel 18:28

Reflection Question:

Absalom was deceived in his rebellion. He had a plan to take over David's kingdom but his life was cut short. Once again, God delivered David. Only this time, the delivery was from the hand of his own son and we see a broken hearted David crying, "my son, my son, my son."

Have you been betrayed by a loved one? Though it is heartbreaking to walk through betrayal, what is worse is never seeing the person come out of their rebellion. Have you lost someone you love? Though your heart may be broken, God is for you. He will never leave you nor forsake you. Praise God today for his faithfulness to you.

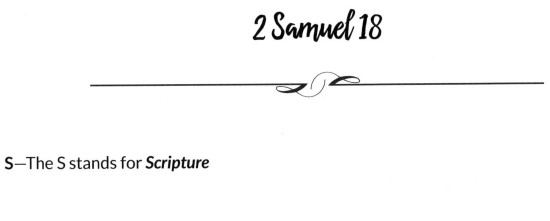

S—The S stands for *Scripture*

O—The O stands for *Observation*

A—The A stands for *Application*

K—The K stands for *Kneeling in Prayer*

Do therefore what seems good to you.

2 Samuel 19:27

Reflection Question:

Mephibosheth was completely devoted to King David. He was so devoted that he did not care about his own wants or desires. He watched and waited for his return. He looked for the King. He longed for the King and he loved the King.

How are you like Mephibosheth? Are you watching and waiting for the return of Christ? Do you look for, long for and love the King of Kings? How can you live more fully focused on God rather than your own wants and desires?

S—The S stands for *Scripture*

O—The O stands for *Observation*

A—The A stands for *Application*

K—The K stands for *Kneeling in Prayer*

He answered, "I am listening."

2 Samuel 20:17

Reflection Question:

A wise woman came out of nowhere and challenged the thinking of the military leader, Joab. She cried, "listen!" and he listened. What great courage this wise woman must have had to show up in this way—uninvited.

Is there someone in your life, headed for a crisis, whom you need to challenge in their thinking? We must tread lightly and prayerfully, as we confront others but we must also not give into fear. There is a time to be silent and a time to speak up. Pray and ask the Lord to show what time it is.

S—The S stands for *Scripture*

O—The O stands for *Observation*

A—The A stands for *Application*

K—The K stands for *Kneeling in Prayer*

David sought the face of the Lord.

2 Samuel 21:1

Reflection Question:

After a famine in the land went on and on and on, David finally sought God. CS Lewis said: "God whispers to us in our pleasures, speaks in our consciences, but shouts in our pains. It is his megaphone to rouse a deaf world."

God uses difficulties and trials to turn our hearts toward him. What pain or trial has God used in your life to get your attention and how have you sought and found God in the midst of your difficulty?

2 Samuel 21

S—The S stands for *Scripture*

O—The O stands for *Observation*

A—The A stands for *Application*

K—The K stands for *Kneeling in Prayer*

The Lord is my rock and my fortress

and my deliverer, my God,

my rock, in whom I take refuge.

2 Samuel 22:2

Reflection Question:

David lists all the things that God is to him. He gives him title after title, as he praises God.

What is God to you? Give God praise by listing some of the titles you have for God below.

2 Samuel 22

S—The S stands for *Scripture*

O—The O stands for *Observation*

A—The A stands for *Application*

K—The K stands for *Kneeling in Prayer*

He dawns on them like the morning light,

like the sun shining forth

on a cloudless morning.

2 Samuel 23:4

Reflection Question:

As David reflects on his life, though it was far from perfect, he remembers how blessed he was. God was always with him and never forsook him. Like a glorious sunrise, after a dark night, were the blessings of God in his life.

Pause for a moment and consider the most beautiful sunrise you have ever seen. Where were you? Now compare that to the blessings you have received in your life despite the imperfections. How are God's blessings like a sunrise in your life?

S—The S stands for **Scripture**

O—The O stands for **Observation**

A—The A stands for **Application**

K—The K stands for **Kneeling in Prayer**

I will not offer burnt offerings

to the Lord my God

that cost me nothing.

2 Samuel 24:24

Reflection Question:

David sinned by numbering his people and attempting to take credit and glory, for the growth of his kingdom. God punished David. David desired to be back in fellowship with God and so he built an altar. Araunah offered to give David what he needed for his sacrifice but David knew that his sacrifice must cost him something if it was going to please God.

Following God comes with a cost. Is there something you need to give up so you can live a more obedient life to God? What has following God cost you? Remember what we gain far outweighs any sacrifice we could ever give.

S—The S stands for *Scripture*

O—The O stands for *Observation*

A—The A stands for *Application*

K—The K stands for *Kneeling in Prayer*

Made in the USA
San Bernardino, CA
24 March 2018